CW00419302

1989 SUPPLEMENT
to
POSTCARDS
of the
FALKLAND ISLANDS
A Catalogue: 1900-1950

by
Henry and Frances Heyburn

SPFI-A

3918 Leland Roa
Louisville, Kentucky 40207
U.S.A.

First published in Great Britain by
Picton Publishing (Chippenham) Ltd. 1989
ISBN 0 948251 40 9

Photoset in AM International Times
Text paper supplied by Howard Smith Papers, Bristol
Printed in Great Britain by Picton Print
Citadel Works, Bath Road, Chippenham, Wilts

PP58149

Title page: BD-1-bd

Table of Contents

Introduction

It is a universally recognized rule that until something is *in print* it is not worthy of serious attention, but once printed is considered to be correct, permanent and attention worthy. So it was with our book, *Postcards of the Falkland Islands, A Catalogue: 1900–1950.* Once printed and published the response in terms of new postcards, additions, corrections and questions began to flow in.

It has been truly exciting to find new cards of existing Series, not to mention whole new Series. As in the case of the original Catalogue this Supplement started as a 'little list', but once new information started coming in, we realized that only a formal Supplement would do the job.

As a consequence of a review of the original Catalogue in the 'Tonsbergs Blad' in Norway, we have had many interesting letters and new postcards from that country. Moreover, in April 1987 we went to Norway and interviewed a number of those who had written. This produced an unusual number of very interesting new postcards of South Georgia and the whaling industry. It also forced us to adopt a rule that general scenes on board floating factories or at sea, that had no clear Falkland connection, were not to be included in this Supplement. (Two did slip into the original Catalogue).

We have also held to the policy of not including postcards of, (1) Falkland related exploring expeditions, (2) 1914 Battle of the Falkland Islands, and, (3) mail ships serving the Falklands from Europe. However, we are happy to report that others are working on catalogues of Antarctic expeditions and mail steamers.

When the original Catalogue was published we thought there might be another fifty to seventy-five cards out there waiting to be discovered. This Supplement contains seventy-eight, so we won't predict a limit on any further discoveries. All we are certain of is that there *will* be more.

Last but not least, we want to report another memorable trip to London and the Falklands in June 1985 to 'kick-off' the original Catalogue. It was a whirlwind tour that included not only Stanley but Goose Green, radio interviews in London (BBC) and Stanley (FIBS), an autograph party attended by Governor and Lady Hunt, a party for our Kelper helpers and much, much more.

And to all, please continue to send your new postcards, corrections, suggestions and questions!

H.R.H. and F.S.H.

Acknowledgements

Again, we must express a dual 'Thank you' to the membership of the Falkland Island Philatelic Study Group *and* to our friends in the Falklands.

To the following individuals who responded to our appeal for new postcards, loan of postcards, corrections and comments, and have provided additional assistance since the original Catalogue went to press, we are greatly indebted.

Australia: Dudley Colville.
Chile: A. D. King, British Consul, Punta Arenas.

Canada: Eric Lawson, Laurie Nock, Amanda Smith.

Falkland Islands: Kitty Bertrand, Madge Biggs, M.B.E., Lewis Clifton, A. B. Hadden, Wallace & Mary Hirtle, Sir Rex M. Hunt & Lady Hunt, Ian & Eileen Jaffray, Sydney & Bet Miller, John Smith, Terry & Joan Spruce.

France: A. Jacob Dijkstra, Michael Druez.

Germany: Klaus Barthclmess, Rolf Kardel, Dieter Kusgen, Bernd Lukas, Manfred Wilke-Ecker, .

New Zealand: Karl V. Lellman, Mrs. R.B.M. Whyle.

Norway: Tore Asplin, Tor Buaas, Bjarne Berg, Thomas E. Binnie, Tore Clason, Jan Erik, Odd Galteland, Edith Martin Nilsen, Nils N. Nilsen, Gunnar Stenersen.

Sweden: Fred Goldberg, Stefan Heijtz.

United Kingdom: R.F. Barnes, Malcolm Barton, A.G. Belfield, Cmdr. David Bird, Donald C. Boyd, D.A. Britton, Pauline Brookes, Gordon A. Buchan, John P. Bunt, J.P. Burkett, Kenneth Burley, Alastair Cameron, William Hunter & Merle Christie, Maj. R.H. Coleman, Alan Cooper, Julian Dunn, H.E.J. Evans, G.R. Garbutt, R.C. Gee, Aubrey Halpern, R.K. Headland, Peter High, Rev. J.N.T. Howat, Richard A. Julian, Nigel Kaye, J.F. Ladbury, Tom Lloyd, Bill Lynch, Dr. Bruce Marsden, Frank Mitchell, R. Murdie, Mrs. E.N. Neild, Francis W. Plowman, Malcolm Richardson, Lee Rouillier, A.M. Rutter, J.L. Shaw, Nicholas Startup, M.A. Sturge, Aubrey Summers, D.C. Styles, Alan Tew, W.P. Vevers, Margery Wharton, P.J. Wordie, Frank Laycock.

United States: Robert W. & Marian Allen, Arthur T. Brown, J. Stephen Dibbern, Janice Harvis, David Larsen, Michael Kerschbaum, Dr. Peter P. McCann, F.L. Oldenberg, Dempsey J. Prappas, William E. Robertson, Stephen R. Schmidt, Robert W. Stewart.

Museums, and Libraries: Scott Polar Research Institute, Cambridge; Sandefjord Whaling Museum, Sandefjord, Norway; Vestfold Fylkesmuseum, Tonsberg, Norway; Congregacion Salesiana, Instituto 'Don Bosco', Punta Arenas,

Chile; St. Bride Printing Library, London; Staats und Universitatsbibliothek Hamburg, Hamburg, Germany; Hedemarkmuseet, Hamar, Norway; Senat Den Freien Und Hansestadt Hamburg-Staatsarchiv.

Once again, the tasks of original typing, arranging, corresponding and dozens of other details were handled with great skill by Rosemary L. Sandman. Thanks are also due to the word processing crew at Brown, Todd & Heyburn for the prompt and efficient way in which they turned out many, many drafts until all was letter perfect.

Explanation of The Catalogue System

How to Read It. How It Works. How To Find Things.
Reprinted from 1985 Edition of Catalogue.
See further explanation beginning on page 11 of this Supplement

All cards are classified in *three steps* as follows:

(1) **Series** (picture side) lettered A through Z, AA through AZ and BA through BO followed by the

(2) **Number** of the card within the series in *alphabetical order of the card's title,* excluding 'A', 'An' or 'The' in determining that order; except Series U and AF which follow the numbers on the postcards; followed by the

(3) **Type** (address side) lettered a through z, aa through az and ba through bo. (Within some Types there are **Sub-types** for which a second or third letter is added as will be described later).

SERIES

Series is determined basically by style of lettering in the title and method of reproducing the picture and is the *predominant side* in identifying any postcard. As nearly as possible, series have been lettered in *chronological order of publication.* If the postcard itself or a contemporary source does not provide the date of publication, the earliest known postmark or date on a postcard message was used.

It should also be noted that if there is any difference at all in wording or spelling of the title, or position of the title, or colour (or lack of it) on the picture side, a different number is given to that card. For example: In Series N, postcard titled

— 'General View of Stanley, Shewing Shipping', is number 3;
and postcard titled

— 'General View of Stanley, Showing Shipping', is number 4

Likewise, in Series B., postcard titled

— 'View of Port Stanley from Christ Church Cathedral Tower',
is number 19; and postcard titled

— 'View of Stanley from Christ Church Cathedral Tower', is number 21

In Series AQ there are glossy sepia and coloured postcards of Whalebone Arch numbered 19 and 20 respectively.

There are frequent examples of the same picture being used on a number of postcards. For example, the identical photograph of the Try Works at Port Stephens is used on D-9-d, D-14-d and L-8-1, but with different wording and position of the title.

One other feature has been added to the description of each series and that is the Key Word(s) System. In order to make it easier to *identify and remember* each series, a few words have been selected which give a capsule description of the particular series. It is shown on the first line after the series (letter(s) and is used in the Index at the front of the Catalogue which also indicates the date and number of cards in each series. Often it is simply the name of the publisher, e.g., R. & A. Hardy, T. & N. Binnie, Ray Hardy, Pettersen, Kwasny or Larsen, to name a few; or it relates to the style of printing, viz, Serif Gothic, Block, Script, etc., or the source such as Saxony, Printed in Great Britain and 'British Manufacture'. It is hoped that these key word descriptions of series will prove helpful in remembering them.

TYPE

Type is determined by the printing style and layout of the *address side.* However, although there are no sub-groupings within the Series, within Types minor differences in layout or printing, called Sub-types, are indicated by the letters z, y, x, w, etc. (in reverse order), following the type letter or letters.

> For example, Type a has a total of three Sub-types which are designated a, az and ay. On the other hand, Type aq has a total of eleven Sub-types which are designated aq, aqz, aqy, aqx, aqw, aqv, aqu, aqt, aqs, aqr and aqq. However, Type aq is an exception. There are rarely more than three Sub-types.
>
> Where Sub-types are involved, the differences in wording or layout are described under the 'Type' heading of the catalogue. Moreover, all types and sub-types are illustrated.

Under this cataloguing system the Series and Type designations are *nearly always* the same letter, but occasionally a series of cards will have been published using some of the same Type as in another series, or perhaps with a variety of Types within that series. However, this doesn't happen often. An example is Series AC which includes both Types ab and ac and Sub-types of the latter.

To summarize, a series of cards and corresponding Types, will be catalogued as follows:

B-5-b Government House, Port Stanley, F.I.
B-6-bz Manager's House, Port Howard, W.F.

Note again that the number assigned to each card is based on the *alphabetical order of title* within the series, excluding 'A', 'An' or 'The' in determining that order.

The few cards with no title are numbered at the end of the series in which they appear and the subject matter is briefly described in parenthesis where the title would normally be. For example, see AQ-21 and AQ-22.

'Short' catalogue number: With very few exceptions the series letter and postcard number alone, e.g. A-3, will completely identify a particular card. It is only when the same card (series and number) has been published with more than one Type (address side) that the Type letters are necessary to completely identify the card. For an example of this see AA-1-aa and AA-1-aaz. *However,* the Type letter does instantly tell which Type is used for a particular card.

HOW TO IDENTIFY A POSTCARD

At the end of the catalogue there is an Alphabetical Index by Title of each postcard. Surprisingly enough, in spite of many similarities of subject matter, in only a few cases are two titles exactly the same and even when they are, the type face or location of the title will allow a distinction to be made. Last but not least, the pictures themselves are usually different.

In addition there is a Subject Index and an Index of Publishers.

ABBREVIATIONS

A/S – Norwegian for incorporated
B.A.S. – British Antarctic Survey
F.I.C. – Falkland Islands Company
F.I.G.A.S – Falkland Islands Government Air Service
F.I.M. – Falkland Islands Magazine and Church Paper
P.S.N.C. – Pacific Steam Navigation Company
R.M.S. – Royal Mail Ship

UL – upper left	UC – upper centre	UR – upper right
LL – lower left	LC – lower centre	LR – lower right

FURTHER EXPLANATION OF SUPPLEMENT

The catalogue numbers in this 1989 Supplement follow the same system as in the original Catalogue except that it has not been possible to list the new cards in each Series in overall alphabetical order.

A list of all NEW postcards will be found on page 13.
A list of CORRECTED postcards will be found on page 15.
A list of postcards PREVIOUSLY LISTED BUT NOT ILLUSTRATED in original Catalogue which are illustrated in this Supplement will be found on page 15.

NEW means just what it says, a completely new postcard never before listed. It can involve a new illustration, title or colour or a card which is new because of an additional Type. In the case of an additional Type the 'newness' may not be readily apparent because in some cases both the Series and the Type already exist but not in the new combination. Examples of this are: **AA-3-aaz, AA-4-aay, AA-3-aaz** and **AA-4-aaz.** Numbers of new postcards are in heavy type.

CORRECTED refers to a postcard which was not correctly described in the original Catalogue. It usually involves a correction in the Type. For example: B-2-b has been corrected to B-2-bz. In fact, since three additional Types under the 'b' category have been found, namely bz, by and bx, 16 out of 25 corrected Types will be found in this 'b' category. Other examples of corrections are: B-3-b becomes B-3-bz; D-2-d becomes D-2-dy; N-2-n becomes N-2-ny.

ADDITIONAL COMMENT has to do with recently discovered facts of interest. It does *not* involve a new or corrected postcard. For example see: AB-10-ab, Series AF, AR-11-ar.

Both Title and Subject Indexes to all new postcards, as well as Index of New Publishers, will be found at the end of this Supplement.

Catalogue numbers of **NEW** and **CORRECTED** postcards are listed in heavy type, e.g. **A-6-ax.**

List of New Postcards

A-6-ax
B-13-by
B-15-bx
B-22-by
B-23-bz
D-16-d
D-17-d
D-18-d
E-12-e
G-4-g
G-5-g
G-6-g
J-2-j
J-2-jz
J-3-j
J-3-jy
J-4-j
J-5-j
K-4-lz
L-10-1
L-11-l
M-4-mz
M-5-m
N-8-n
O-2-nz
Q-14-q
Q-15-q
Q-16-q
Q-17-q
T-4-tz
Y-6-y
Z-7-z
AA-3-aay
AA-4-aaz
AA-5-aaz
AC-7-ab
AC-8-ac
AC-17-ac
AE-9-ae
AE-10-ae
AH-7-blank
AI-4-ai
AI-5-ai
AI-6-ai
AI-7-ai
AI-8-ai
AL-5-al
AL-6-al
AL-7-al
AL-8-al
AL-9-al
AL-10-al
AQ-23-aqv
AR-20-ar
AR-21-ar
BD-1-bd
BD-2-bd
BE-1-be
BE-2-be
BE-3-be
BE-4-be
BE-5-be
BF-1-bf
BG-1-bg
BG-2-bg
BH-1-bh
BI-l-bi
BJ-l-bj
BK-1-bk
BK-2-bk
BK-3-bk
BK-4-bk
BK-5-bk
BL-l-bl
BM-1-bm
BN-1-bn
BO-1-bo
BO-2-bo

★ ★ ★ ★

List of Corrected Postcards

New Number	**Old Number**
B-2-bz	B-2-b
B-3-bz	B-3-b
B-4-bz	B-4-b

New Number	Old Number
B-5-by	B-5-b
B-7-by	B-7-b
B-8-bz	B-8-b
B-9-by	B-9-b
B-10-bz	B-10-b
B-11-bz	B-11-b
B-12-bz	B-12-b
B-14-by	B-14-b
B-16-bx	B-16-b
B-17-bz	B-17-b
B-18-bz	B-18-b
B-20-by	B-20-b
B-21-by	B-21-b
D-2-dy	D-2-d
F-2-f – Title Correction Add 'Falkland Islands'	
N-2-ny	N-2-n
T-13-tz – Title Correction Add 'On' to title	T-13-t
Z-5-z – Title Correction to 'The Most Sourtherly Church South Georgia'	
AA-4-aay	AA-4-aa
AD-5-adz	AD-5-ad
AD-6-adz	AD-6-ad
BB-2-bbz	BB-2-bb

★ ★ ★ ★

Previously Listed but not Illustrated

B-3-bz	AB-7-ab
E-8-e	AB-10-ab
E-10-e	AC-5-ac
L-6-1	AC-7-acz
	AC-13-acz
T-l-t	AD-1-ad
T-2-tz	AD-5-adz
T-8-t	AD-6-adz
U-18-u	AH-2-aqs
V-1-v	AI-3-ai

V-2-vz
V-5-v
AA-3-aaz
AA-4-aay

AR-2-ar
AR-7-ar
AR-11-ar
AR-14-ar
AT-3-at

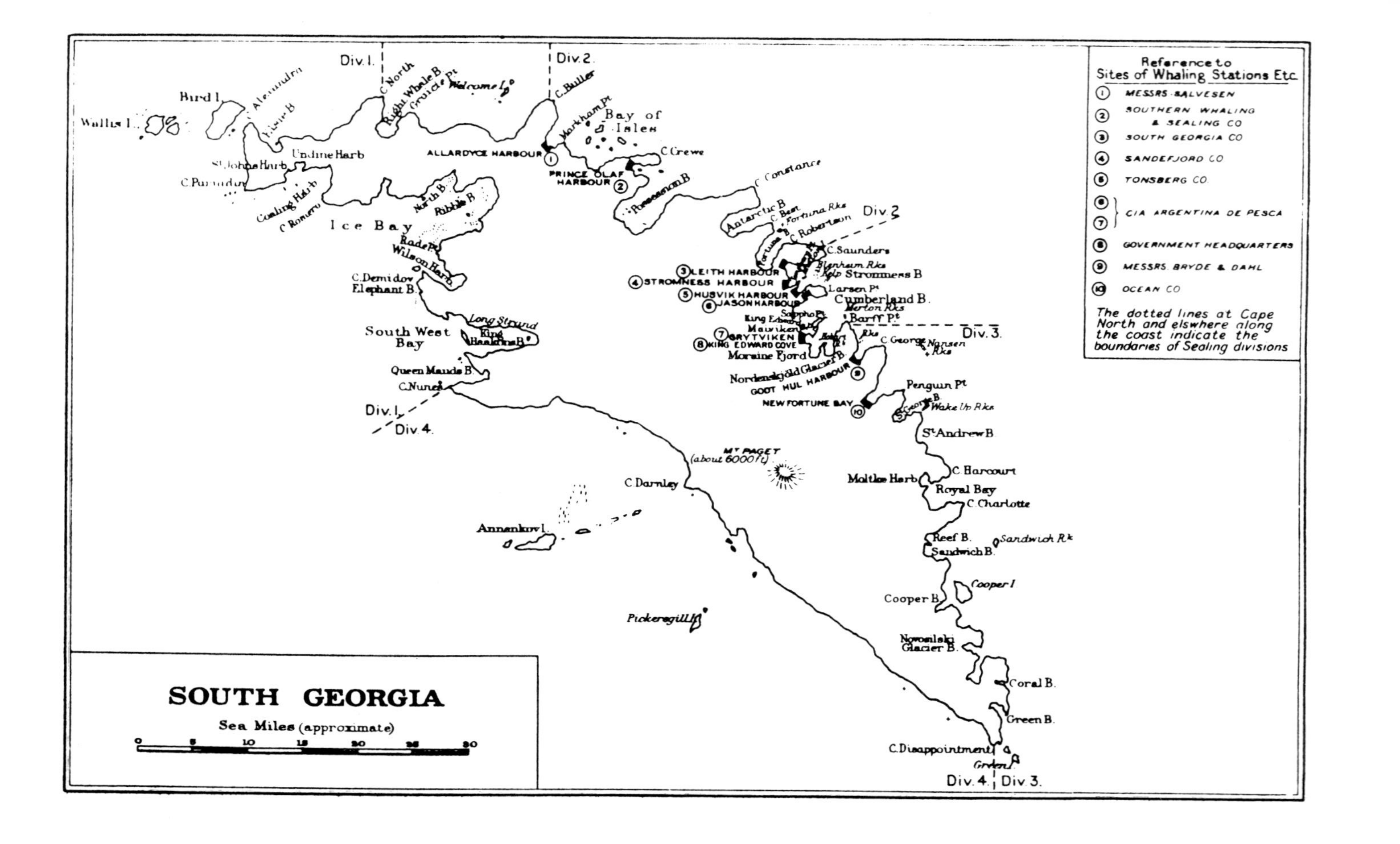

SOUTH GEORGIA
Sea Miles (approximate)
0 5 10 15 20 25 30
Reference to Sites of Whaling Stations Etc.
1 MESSRS SALVESEN
2 SOUTHERN WHALING & SEALING CO
3 SOUTH GEORGIA CO
4 SANDEFJORD CO
5 TONSBERG CO
6, 7 CIA ARGENTINA DE PESCA
8 GOVERNMENT HEADQUARTERS
9 MESSRS. BRYDE & DAHL
10 OCEAN CO
The dotted lines at Cape North and elswhere along the coast indicate the boundaries of Sealing divisions
Div. 1.
Div. 2.
Div. 3.
Div. 4.
Bird I.
Wallis I.
Alexandra
Elsie B
St Johns Harb
C. Paryadin
Undine Harb
Coaling Harb
C. Romero
C. North
Right Whale B.
Groicte Pt
Welcome I.
C. Buller
Markham Pt
Bay of Isles
ALLARDYCE HARBOUR
PRINCE OLAF HARBOUR
C. Crewe
Possession B.
C. Constance
North B.
Ribble B.
Ice Bay
Rade Pt
Wilson Harb
C. Demidov
Elephant B.
Long Strand
South West Bay
King Haakons B.
Queen Mauds B.
C. Nunez
Antarctic B.
C. Best
Fortuna Rks
Fortuna B
C. Robertson
C. Saunders
Blenheim Rks
Kelp
Stromness B
LEITH HARBOUR
STROMNESS HARBOUR
HUSVIK HARBOUR
JASON HARBOUR
Larsen Pt
Cumberland B.
Merton Rks
Barff Pt
Sappho Pt
King Edward
Maiviken
GRYTVIKEN
KING EDWARD COVE
Moraine Fjord
C. George
Nansen Rks
Nordenskjöld Glacier B.
GOOT HUL HARBOUR
NEW FORTUNE BAY
Penguin Pt
St George B.
Wake Up Rks
St Andrew B
Mt PAGET (about 6000 ft)
C. Harcourt
Moltke Harb
Royal Bay
C. Charlotte
C. Darnley
Annenkov I.
Reef B.
Sandwich B.
Sandwich Rk
Cooper I
Cooper B.
Pickersgill I.
Novosilski Glacier B.
Coral B.
Green B.
C. Disappointment
Green I.

Publisher: Albert Aust, Hamburg

A-6-ax Stanley, Falkland Islands (LL).

A-6-ax

A

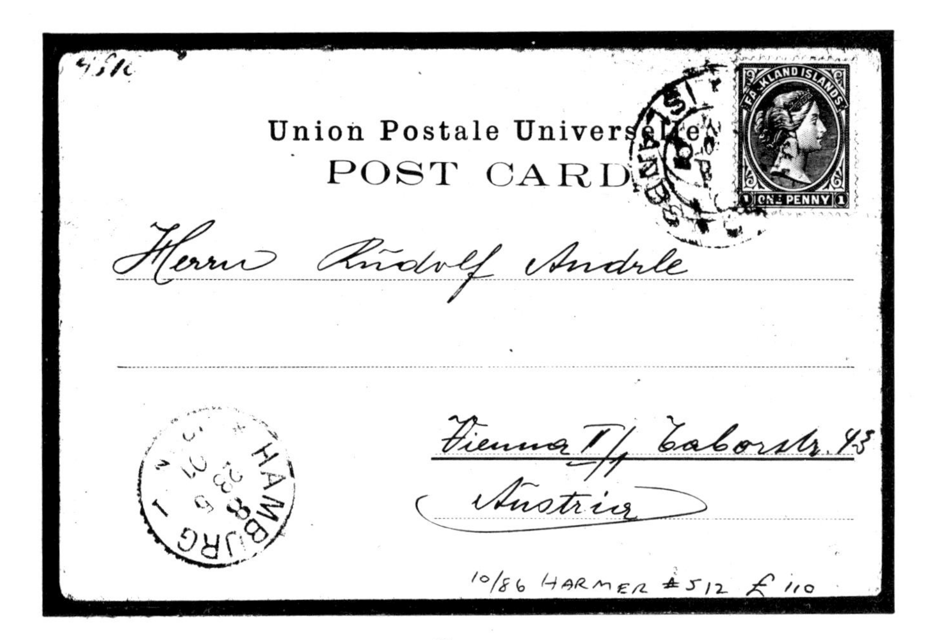

Type ax
Same as Type a except black ink.

Publisher: George P. Biggs, Stanley.

Comment: When the original Catalogue was published the authors overlooked the fact that not one but four different Types, i.e. address sides, were used in printing Series B. Thanks to W.P. Vevers and R.F. Barnes the three additional types were identified. Thus in addition to Type b, there are three new Types, namely, bz, by and bx, illustrated below, which have resulted in sixteen corrections. There are also four new postcards.

Correction: B-2-b becomes **B-2-bz,** Christ Church Cathedral. (LL), Port Stanley. (LR, vertical).

B-3-bz
Previously listed but not illustrated.

Correction: B-3-b becomes **B-3-bz,** Falkland Islands Co.'s Stores. (LL), Port Stanley. (LR).

Correction: B-4-b becomes **B-4-bz,** Government House. (LL), Port Stanley. (LR).

Correction: B-5-b becomes **B-5-by,** Herring Fishing, Port Stanley. (LL)

Correction: B-7-b becomes **B-7-by,** Laying Foundation Stone of St. Mary's Chapel. (LL).

B

Correction: B-8-b becomes **B-8-bz,** Malvina House (LL) Port Stanley. (LR).

Correction: B-9-b becomes **B-9-by**, Proclamation of King Edward VII., 1901. (LL).

Correction: B-10-b becomes **B-10-bz,** Roman Catholic Church (LL), Port Stanley. (LR, vertical).

Correction: B-11-b becomes **B-11-bz,** Shipping and View of Entrance. (LL), Port Stanley. (LR).

Correction: B-12-b becomes **B-12-bz,** Stanley Cottage. (LL) Port Stanley. (LR).

B-13-by View of Port Stanley. (LL)
View is from south east, rocks in foreground.

Correction: B-14-b becomes **B-14-by,** View of Port Stanley. (LL).
Jubilee Villas and Public Jetty

B-15-bx View of Port Stanley, F.I. (LL) Both B-15-b and B-15-bx are coloured.
Government Jetty.

Correction: B-16-b becomes **B-16-bx** View of Port Stanley F.I. (LL), coloured.
Photo same as N-5-n and AV-3-avz, Government House at right.

Correction: B-17-b becomes **B-17-bz,** View of Port Stanley, F.I. (LL).
John St. looking West.

Correction: B-18-b becomes **B-18-bz,** View of Port Stanley, F.I. (LL).
Sign 'Charles Williams' on stone house at John and Philomel Street.

Correction: B-20-b becomes **B-20-by,** View of Port Stephens Settlement, West Falklands. (LL).

Correction: B-21-b becomes **B-21-by,** View of Stanley from Christ Church Cathedral Tower. (LL).
Same photo as B-19-b but without 'Port' in title.

B-22-by Penguin Rookery, Port Stanley (LL).
Same photo as B-6-b but different title.

B-23-bz View of Port Stanley, F.I. (LL).
Looking east down harbour, Government House at right.

★ ★ ★ ★

B

POST CARD

THE ADDRESS ONLY TO BE WRITTEN ON THIS SIDE.

INLAND
½d.
STAMP
FOREIGN
1d.

Type b

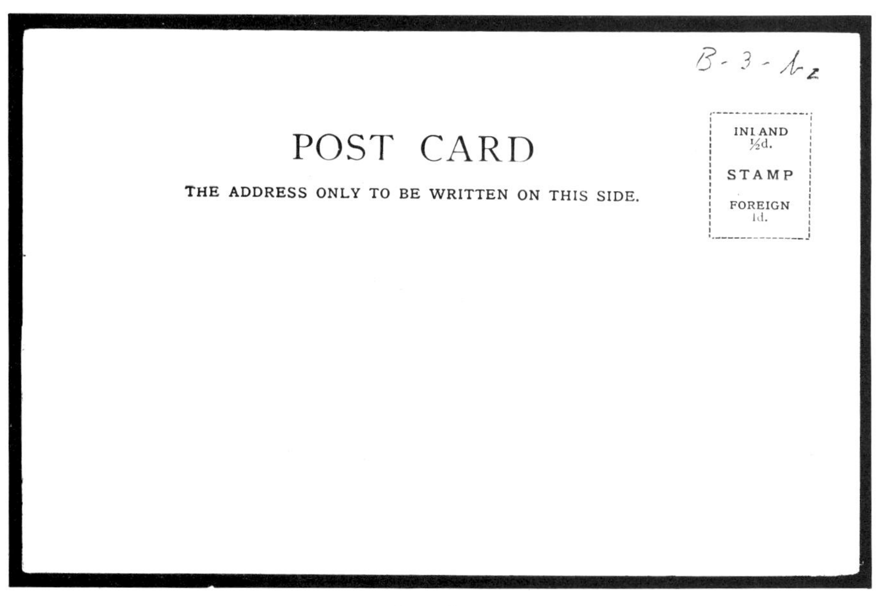

Type bz

B

POST CARD

THE ADDRESS ONLY TO BE WRITTEN ON THIS SIDE.

INLAND
½d.
STAMP
FOREIGN
1d.

Type by

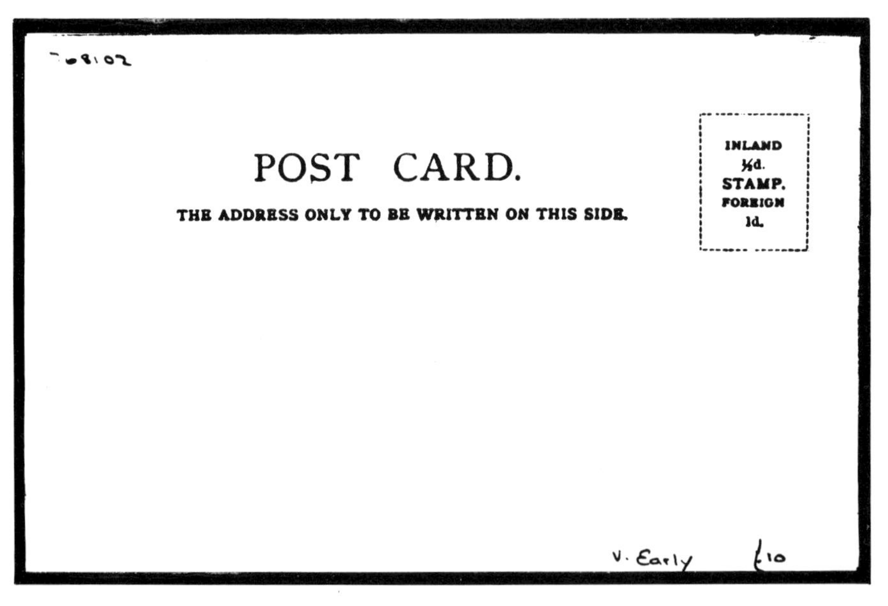

Type bx

The four types are illustrated and the differences described as follows:

Type b Period after POST CARD. Period after word 'side' in second line. Straight horizontal line used in ½ *d. and single space above and below word STAMP in stamp box.*

Type bz *No period after POST CARD. Period after word 'side' in second line. Slanting line used in ½d. and double space above and below word STAMP in stamp box.*

Type by *No period after POST CARD. Period after word 'side' in second line. Straight horizontal line used in ½ d. and double space above and below word 'STAMP' in stamp box.*

Type bx *Period after POST CARD. Period after word 'side' in second line. Slanted line used in ½d. and lines in stamp box are single spaced above and below word 'STAMP'. Also note wide margin at top. Top of words POST CARD is 13/16 of an inch from the top of card.*

Publisher: T. & N. Binnie, Stanley.

Correction: D-2-d becomes **D-2-dy,** General View of Stanley, Falkland Islands (LL).

D-16-d Port Stanley, F.I. (LC).
Same photo and border as D-11-dz but with different title and block printing.

D-17-d Sea Lion Rookery, Falkland Islands (LC).
Same photo and border as L-10-1 and L-10-1z. Also same photo as D-12-d but latter has more beach in foreground.

D-18-d Government House, Port Stanley, F. I. (LC)

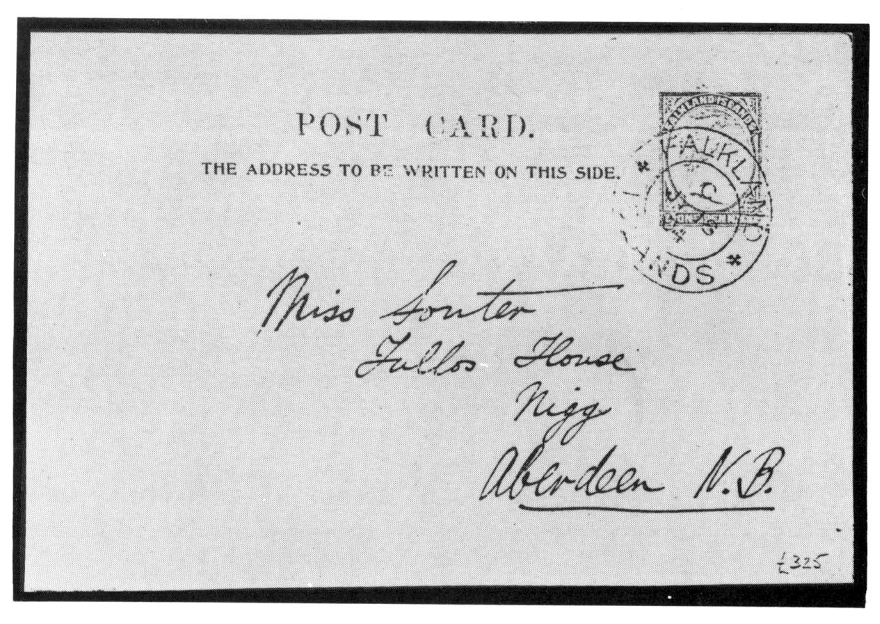

Type dy

Publisher: Unknown.

E-8-e
Previously listed but not illustrated.

E-12-e Falkland Islands (LL) Stanley, looking North-East from Hill (LR).

E-10-e
Previously listed but not illustrated.

Publisher: Unknown.

Correction: F-2-f becomes Jubilee Villas & Cathedral, Stanley, Falkland Islands (LL).

Publisher: Unknown

Comment: With discovery of three additional postcards in this Series G, the previous title, 'Three-Card Sequence', has been changed to 'Harbour Sequence'.

G-4-g Port Stanley (LC).
Falkland Islands Co. office.

G-4-g

G-5-g Port Stanley (LC).
Jubilee Villas.

G-6-g Port Stanley (LC).
Government House.

G

Iles Falkland
2 Août 1904.

Nous nous trouvons ici dans une de ces admirables forteresses anglaises, merveilleusement située et des plus faciles à défendre, mais qu'il fait froid ! Maurice

G-6-g

J-2-j
J-2-jz

Roqueria de Penguines de la Tierra Adelia-Islas Orcadas, Republica Argentina (LC).
(Adelie Penguin Rookery, South Orkneys).
Men with skis in right foreground.

J-2-j and J-2-jz

J-3-j
J-3-jy

Roqueria de Penguines antarticos – Islas Orcadas, Republica Argentina.
(Antartic Penguin Rookery, South Orkneys) (LC).
Many penguins on rocks.

J-4-j

La Cabana y el observatorio Argentino. Islas Orcadas.
(Argentine hut and weather station. South Orkneys) (LC).

J-5-j

Foca blanca – Islas Orcadas, Republica Argentina. (White Seal) (LC).
Appears to be a crabeater, the most common seal in Antarctica.

J-3-j and J-3-jy

J-5-j

J

1251. Editor R. Rosauer, Rivadavia 571 Buenos Aires. Neg. del Sr L. H. Valette.

Tarjeta postal.
Carte postale.
Union postale universelle.

Franqueo
Interior 4 c.
Exterior 6 c.

Type jy

TARJETA POSTAL

J-2-jz

Type jz

Publisher: T & N Binnie, Stanley.

K-4-lz Penguin Rookery, Falklands (UL).
Two penguins in centre and right foreground. Very large group in background.

Publisher: T. & N. Binnie, Stanley.

L-6-1

Previously listed but not illustrated.

L-10-1 Sea Lion Rookery, Falkland Islands (LC).
Front same as L-10-lz and D-17-c.

L-11-1 Port Stanley and Part of Harbour. (LL).
Picture and frame same as D-3-d, but with different title.

M-4-mz Port Stanley – Falkland Island (LL) A.K., Punta Arenas – Magallanes – Chile (LR).
This card same as M-2-mz except that publisher's name at LR is printed as follows: A. K. Punta-Arenas de Magallanes-Chile.

M-5-m Port Stanley – Falkland-Island (LC).
Same as M-3-m except that photo is tinted green.

Publisher: Estate Louis Williams.

Correction: N-2-n becomes **N-2-ny,** General View of Stanley Looking N.W. from Hill. (UL).

N-6-n General View of Stanley – Winter (UL).
View from South east. The photo of N-6-n was in the original Catalogue but N-6-n was not listed in the Series.

N-8-n General View of Stanley – North West from Hill. (UL).
Almost same picture as N-2-ny except house on extreme right in N-8-n shows only one chimney.

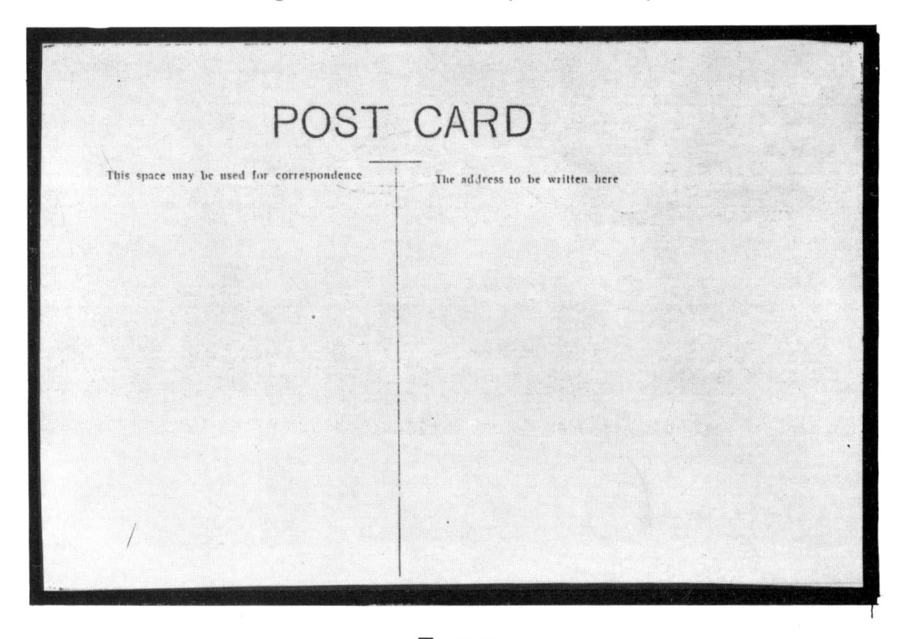

Type ny
Only one line across top of dividing line.

Publisher: Unknown.

O-2-nz View of Stanley from Landing Stage (LR).

O-2-nz

Publisher: S. M. Petterson, Norway.

Q-14-q Sjoelefant fra South Georgia. (UL) (Sea Elephant at South Georgia).

Q-14-q

Q-15-q Hvalfangeren 'Hauken' i storm (UL) (Whale catcher 'Hauken' in storm).

'Hauken' was one of two catchers which accompanied 'Admiralen', the first floating factory to operate in the Antarctic, 1905–1906 season. These ships were based at Admiralty Bay, King George Island, South Shetlands. Alexander Lange was manager of the expedition.

Q-16-q Undine og Tyske Expeditions 'Deutschland' (UL) (Departure of Deutschland Expedition).

'Deutschland' (German South Polar Expedition), under the command of Dr. Wilhelm Filchner, departed from Grytviken, South Georgia on December 11, 1911.

Q-17-q Fra Gryteviken, South Georgia, 'Fos' (Waterfall).

Hvalfangeren „Hauken" i Storm

Q-15-q

Undine og Tyske Ekspeditions „Deutschland"

Q-16-q

Q

Q-17-q

Reproduction: Glossy sepia.

Correction: Type r is brown ink, not black.

Publisher: Printed in Saxony.

T-l-t
Previously listed but not illustrated.

T-4-tz Gentoo Penguin Rookery, Falkland Islands (UL).
Front same as T-4-t but with Type tz address side.

Corrections: T-13-t becomes **T-13-tz.**
Title is also corrected to read, On the Track to Stanley for the Mail (UL).

T-2-tz
Previously listed but not illustrated.

T-8-t
Previously listed but not illustrated.

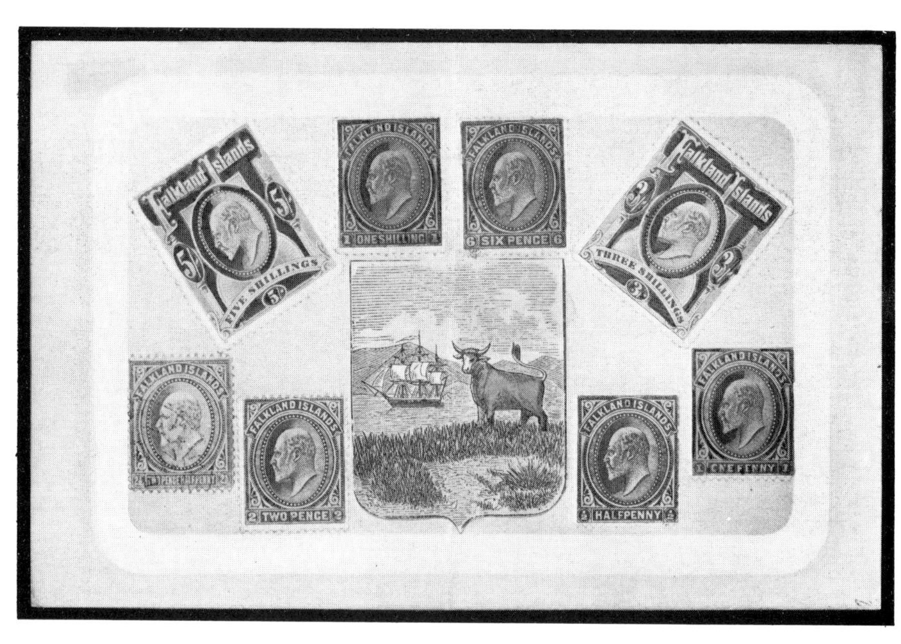

U-18-u
Previously listed but not illustrated.

V-1-v

Previously listed but not illustrated.

Correction: Ink on Types v and vz varies from blue-black to blue green to black.

V-2-vz
Previously listed but not illustrated.

V-5-v
Previously listed but not illustrated.

Y-6-y Ross Road, East, Stanley, Falkland Islands (UL).

Y-6-y

Correction: Z-5-z. Correct title is 'The Most Southerly Church, South Georgia', not, 'A Local Church'.

This church was erected largely through the efforts of C.A. Larsen. It originally stood in Strommen, Norway and was dismantled and moved to Grytviken in 1913. A British magistrate had been appointed at South Georgia in 1909. Thus, after the erection of the church the old whaler's adage, 'Beyond 40° is no law, beyond 50° no God', was not longer true.

Z-7-z The Whaling Industry, Falkland Islands (UC)
Moonlight View of Allardyce Range (LC)
Whale catcher in centre

Publisher: T. & N. Binnie, Stanley, Falkland Islands.

AA-3-aay; and AA-3-aaz which was previously listed but not illustrated.

AA-3-aay Funeral Ceremony of those killed in the Naval action off Falkland Islands, December 8th, 1914. Leaving the Cathedral.
Front same as AA-3-aaz but with Type aay.

AA-4-aaz Liberty Men of HMS 'Good Hope' October 20, 1914 Stanley, F.I.

Correction: AA-4-aa becomes **AA-4-aay,** Liberty Men of H.M.S. 'Good Hope', October 20, 1914 Stanley, F.I.

AA-5-aaz Funeral Ceremony of those killed in the Naval action off Falkland Islands, December 8th, 1914. Procession on the way to the cemetery. Admiral Sturdee marked A. Governor Allardyce marked B.
Front same as AA-5-aa but with Type aaz.

AA

AA-4-aaz; and AA-4-aay which was previously listed but not illustrated.

Publisher: Hoods Engravers and Printers, Middlesbrough, England, under trade mark 'San Bride'.

PORT STANLEY, Falkland Islands.

AB-7-ab

Previously listed but not illustrated.

Additional Comment: AB-10-ab A Sea Elephant, Falkland Islands.

Elephant seals are rarely seen in the Falklands proper. This is probably the sea elephant which died at Darwin and is reported on in the June 1908 Falkland Islands Magazine as follows: "Considerable excitement was recently caused at Darwin by the appearance of a fifteen foot long Sea Elephant. This huge animal got right up the Bay, under the bridge, and finally met his death close to the Wool shed. The entire population turned out to see this unique sight and a syndicate was quickly formed to exhibit it. A well-known taxidermist, being happily on the spot, at once proceeded to make the most of this 'windfall', and we are led to believe that his exertions have been prolonged and arduous, and that the sight of this gentleman skinning this treasure trove, and explaining his beauties to the public was one to remember".

AB

A SEA ELEPHANT, Falkland Islands.

AB-10-ab
Previously listed but not illustrated.

Publisher: Hoods, Engravers and Printers, Middlesbrough, England, under trade mark 'San Bride'.

AC-5-ac
Previously listed but not illustrated.

AC-7-ab Interior Cathedral, Port Stanley.
Front same as AC-7-acz but with Type ab.

AC-8-ac The Old 'Great Britain' Falkland Islands (LL).
Front same as Ac-8-acz but with Type ac. Same photo as P-4-p.

AC-17-ac Government House and Colonial Secretary's Quarters, Stanley, Falkland Islands. (LL).
Same photo as AB-3-ab.

Correction: Type acz has light blue or blue green ink.

Interior Cathedral, Port Stanley, Falkland Islands.

AC-7-ab and AC-7-acz
Previously listed but not illustrated.

Shags, Falkland Islands

AC-13-acz
Previously listed but not illustrated.

Publisher: Ray V. Hardy, Stanley.

Reproduction: Glossy Sepia

AD-1-ad
Previously listed but not illustrated.

Correction: AD-5-ad becomes **AD-5-adz,** Port Stanley, Falkland Islands. (LC).

Correction: AD-6-ad becomes **AD-6-adz,** Port Stanley, Falkland Islands. (LC).

Type ad is brown ink, not black.

Type adz is green ink, not black.

AD-5-adz
Previously listed but not illustrated.

AD-6-adz
Previously listed but not illustrated.

Publisher: 'British Throughout'.

AE-9-ae Bearing body of one of the men of ex HMS 'Kent' to the Cathedral, Stanley. Killed in action with Germans off Falkland Islands, 8.12.14. (LR).

Bearing body of one of the men ex H.M.S. "Kent" to the Cathedral, Stanley. Killed in action with the Germans off Falkland Islands, 8-12-14

AE-9-ae

AE-10-ae The Uruguayan steamer 'Instituto de Pesca' called at Stanley, F.I. 24/6, 1916, to get Sir Ernest Shackleton, and then go S. to look for his lost men in the ice-hole. Showing mutton being made fast to the steamer's mast. (LC vertical)

The Uruguayan ship 'Instituto de Pesca No. 1' was the second ship to try to get through to rescue Shackleton's men marooned on Elephant Island. The first was the whale catcher 'Southern Sky' which left South Georgia May 23, 1916 but didn't get within 60 miles. The third was the 'Emma' from Chile, also unsuccessful. At last, a second Chilean ship, the 'Yelcho', reached the castaways on August 30, 1916.

The Uruguayan steamer "Instituto de Pesca
called at Stanley, F.I. 24/6, 1916, to get Sir
Ernest Shackleton, and then go S. to look for his
'lost men in the ice-hole. Showing mutton
being made fast to the steamer's mast

AE-10-ae

Publisher: Southern Studio, Foto. Magn. Himberg. Prince Olav Harbour, South Georgia.

Correction: Series AF was published at Prince Olav Harbour, South Georgia, not Norway. See under Index of Publishers for details.

Publisher: Various.

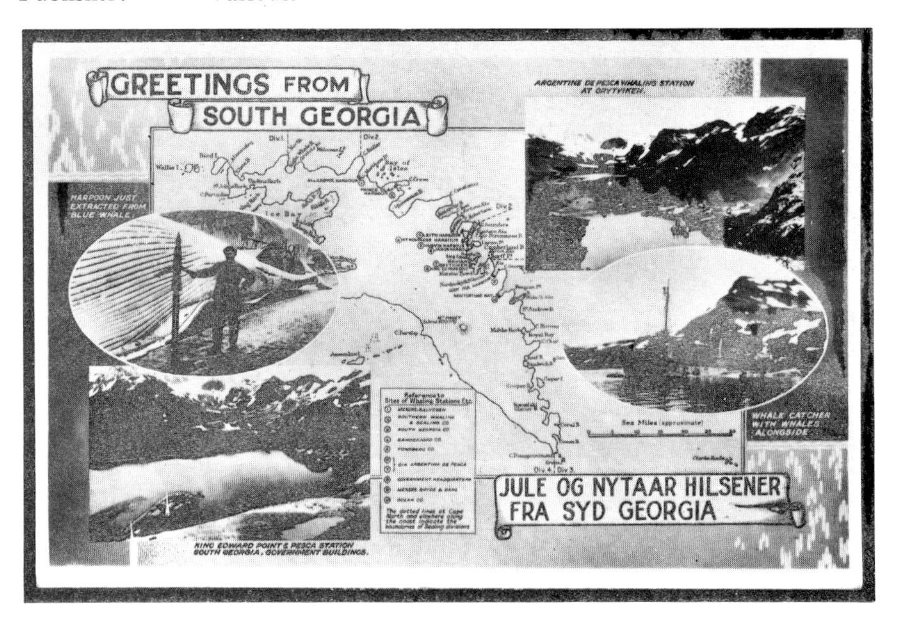

AH-2-aqs
Previously listed but not illustrated.

AH-7-blank Greetings from the Falkland Islands (C).
Six small photos in two rows of three each as follows: View of Stanley (UL), Cape Pembroke Lighthouse (UC), Ross Road (UR), Memorial of Battle of Falkland Islands 1914 (LL), RMS 'Fitzroy' (LC), Cathedral and Whalebone Arch (LR).

AH-7-blank

AI Series AI WEMBLEY 1924

Publisher: British Empire Exhibition.

Additional comment: With the exception of AI-8-ai titles are on both sides.

AI-2-ai
Previously listed but not illustrated

AI-4-ai View of Back of Court Looking West.

AI-5-ai View of Back of Western Part of Court.

AI-6-ai View of Eastern Part of Court as seen from the Western Gangway.

AI-7-ai View of Western Part of Court as seen from the South Gangway.

AI-8-ai Visit of their Majesties to the Falkland Islands Court on the 14th May, 1924, with the King and Queen of Roumania. (Along left edge, address side only).

AI-3-ai
Previously listed but not illustrated

AI-6-ai

Publisher: A. Th. Larsen, Tonsberg, Norway.

Additional comment: A. Th. Larsen of Tunsberg was a prolific publisher of postcards of the whaling industry. Cards numbered as high as 110 have been observed. However, as previously stated (see original Catalogue under AL), many of these are of individual ships or of the processing of whales on shipboard without any specific identification as to location in the Falkland Islands or Dependencies. Although the distinctions are sometimes tenuous, the intention has been to omit all such postcards. AL-3-al and AL-4-al are unintended exceptions.

AL-5-al

AL-5-al Flensning av hval (LL) (Flensing a whale).

AL-6-al Oplemning av hval (LL) (Cutting up a whale).

AL-7-al Pinginer (LL) (Penguins).

AL-8-al Tbg. Hvalfangeris Landstation. Syd-Georgia. (LL).
The Tonsbergs Hvalfangeri landstation at Husvik Harbour was named for the small town of Husvik (outside Tonsberg) where most of the company's whalers lived. Operations were commenced in the 1907-1908 season with a single floating factory, the 'Bucantaur'. The construction of a shore station was completed in

AL-6-al

1913. From then, until the start of the Great Depression in 1931 only the land station operated. After World War II it was reactivated from 1945 to 1960, except for the 1957–1958 season. Albion Star Ltd. (South Georgia Co.) then took over for one last season, 1960–1961.

Husvik Harbour, unlike Leith which suffered at least two major avalanches, was situated on a large flat expanse with no steep, over-hanging mountains. There was an abundant supply of fresh water, an essential requirement for any whaling station. Stromness Harbour, operated by Sandefjord Whaling Co., lay two miles north of Husvik, and two and a half miles north of it was the South Georgia Company's (Salvesen) land station on Leith Harbour. A rough pedestrian track connected the three stations. All of the stations faced east onto the larger Stromness Bay.

AL-9-al Tbg. Hvalfangeris Landstation. Syd-Georgia. (LL).
A whaler's life at Husvik, in fact at all stations, was not an easy one. In summer work was from six in the morning until six in the evening, in winter as long as daylight lasted. There was little entertainment but the men found many hobbies. To quote one manager: 'Seeing all these whalers, one would have through they would be dead tired by evening, but many still had sufficient energy to cultivate their hobby or to make a little extra by making

AL

AL-8-al

AL-9-al

AL-10-al

and selling various articles from the whale's organs. One of them collected whales' eyes, which he hollowed out, drying the skin over a round shape to make the most beautiful parchment-like lampshades. When the skin of the heart had been cleaned and dried, it produced a large piece of parchment over one square metre in area. this could be used for making ladies' handbags, tobacco pouches, etc. Some read and tried to learn languages, others carved figures out of whalebone and out of the teeth of the sperm whale; one made violins; some soled boots and patched clothes; one repaired watches and another cut hair. Most of them would foregather in the mess, and discuss politics and solve the problems of this world over a cup of coffee'. Photography was also a popular hobby which is attested to by the many 'home-made' postcards of excellent quality that were produced.

Food was plentiful. Every season live sheep, pigs, chickens, ducks and geese were brought down to provide fresh meat. Experiments were made with over-wintering sheep in the tussac but they were unable to survive the rigorous winters. That was left to the reindeer (See BO-1-bo) and the rats, both of which thrived.

The everyday needs of the whalers in terms of tobacco, clothing, photographic materials, toiletries, postcards (such as these), stationery and many other items were provided for by a 'slop chest', the whaleman's version of the company store.

AL **AL-10-al** Tbg. Hvalfangeris Landstation. Syd-Georgia. (LL).

At Husvik and other stations, except for accidents, there were few medical problems. An exception was the arrival of the summer whaling crews in November which invariably brought flu with them. Accidents were hard to avoid given the nature of whaling operations, but at an early stage there was a small hospital at each station, and when a major operation was to be performed doctors from adjoining stations would assist. The toll among the catchers was substantial. Nearly thirty of them capsized, were wrecked or sank between 1911 and 1969 with a loss of eighty-six lives. These men found only a 'watery grave' but the neatly tended cemetery at each station was symbolic of the hazards and vicissitudes of a whaleman's life.

AO-1-ao
Previously listed but not illustrated.

AQ-23-aqv Port Stanley, Falkland Islands, From the Air. (LL).
View looking south east; Cathedral at centre.

AQ-23-aqv

AR-2-ar
Previously listed but not illustrated.

Additional Comment :

AR-11-ar Peat Cutting, Port Stanley. In upper left background is flat car of the Camber Railway which connected the Naval Depot with the wireless station. See illustration on next page.

AR-7-ar
Previously listed but not illustrated.

AR-11-ar
Previously listed but not illustrated.

AR-14-ar
Previously listed but not illustrated.

AR-20-ar

AR-20-ar Penguins on the Beach (LL).

AR-21-ar

AR-21-ar Port Stanley West (LL).
Large building in center, with vestibule at left, is The Tabernacle of the United Free Church, on Barrack Street. It opened in 1891 and was then known as the Nonconformist Tabernacle. It is still in use.

AT-3-at
Previously listed but not illustrated.

Correction: BB-2-bb is **BB-2-bbz,** Graham Land Peninsula, Antarctica. The Commonwealth Institute, London. The catalogue number under the postcard picture is correct.

The following Series BD through BO are completely new.

Publisher: Unknown.

Lettering: White.

Reproduction: Photographic.

BD-1-bd

BD-1-bd Fish Point Light, Deception Island, S. Shetlands. The most Southerly Ocean Light in existence. (LC vertical).

There is no such place as Fish Point on Deception. Fildes Point is at north side of Neptune's Bellows. The light is now on southern shore of Port Foster, several hundred yards inside the entrance.

BD-2-bd

BD-2-bd A Land Scene on S. Orkneys (LL).

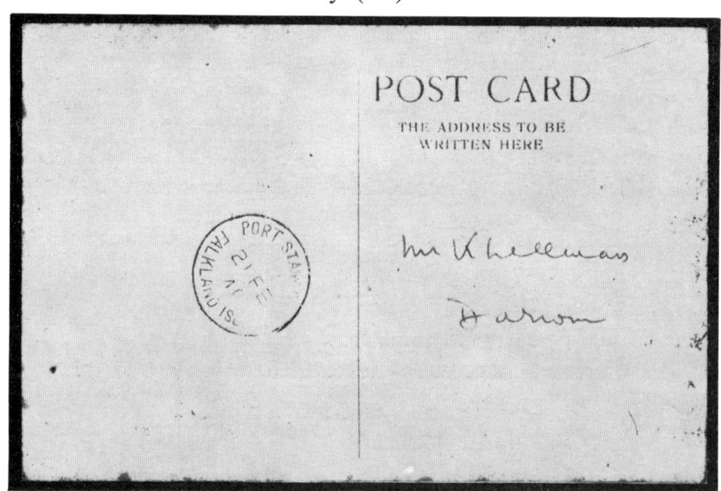

Type bd

Type bd is same as Type p, but without small San Bride along center dividing line.

Publisher: Chr. Wattne, Norway.

Lettering: Same as Series Q.

Reproduction: Photographic.

BE-1-be

BE-1-be Flenseplan, Leith Harbour, Syd Georgia (UL).

BE-2-be Hvalstation, Syd Georgia, Flensning og Kjodskjaering (Whaling Station, South Georgia, Flensing and Cooking) (UC).

BE-3-be Sjo-Elefanter, Syd Georgia (Sea Elephants, South Georgia) (UL).
Large bull at right with curving tail.

BE-4-be Sjo-Elefanter, Syd Georgia (UC).
Large bull at right with head in air.

BE-5-be Spaekskjaering, Syd Georgia (UL).
(Cutting up blubber).

Hualstation, Syd Georgia, Flensning og Kjødskjæring

BE-2-be

Sjø-Elefanter, Syd Georgia

BE-3-be

BE-5-be

Type be

Words, 'Eneret Chr. Wattne', printed along left margin, perpendicular to bottom of postcard.

Publisher:	Norwegian.
Lettering:	Black, Roman, initial caps.
Reproduction:	Unknown - double postcard.

BF-1-bf Hvalstationen, Syd-Georgia (Whaling Station, South Georgia) (UC).
Probably Salvesen Station, Leith Harbour. Ship is 'Coronda'.

Type bf

There is a six digit serial number inside lower border of stamp box. Note that Type af is similar but has serial number in center of box and name of publisher along dividing line.

BF-1-bf

Type bf

Publisher:	Chr. Wattne, Norway.
Lettering:	White.
Reproduction:	Photographic.

BG-1-bg

BG-1-bg Lastet Transporbaad faerdig til afgang S. Georgia (Last Transport Ship ready to leave S. Georgia). Eneret Chr. Wattne (LL) Number 10 at LR.

Probably Leith Harbour. Ship on outside appears to be 'Coronda', and inside her may be 'North Sands'.

BG-2-bg 17. Maitog 1914 S. Georgia (17th of May parade 1914 S. Georgia) (LC) Erneret Chr. Wattne (LL).

May 17 is the anniversary of the Norwegian Constitituion and of the separation of Norway from Denmark, a very important national holiday. 1914 was the 100th anniversary of this event and therefore particularly notable. This is a typical parade but undoubtedly the farthest south. The Norwegian flag is at the front followed by a band and then the whalers. The banners may be of labour unions.

Type bg

Double dividing line is off center to left. Dashed lines for address.

Publisher: Barry Girling and Cathedral Press, Port Stanley.

Lettering: Black, roman, initial caps.

Reproduction: Grey lithograph.

BH-1-bh Christ Church Cathedral, Port Stanley (LC).
View from center aisle looking towards altar. Identical to Z-1-z, except for reference to person holding copyright.

Post Card. BH-1-bh *

Copyright, by Barry Girling.
Printed at the Cathedral Press, Port Stanley. F. I.

2/86 Richardson £12

Type bh

Parallel to left margin in two lines are the words: Copyright, by Barry Girling Printed at the Cathedral Press, Port Stanley, F.I. Except for words 'Barry Girling', Type bh is the same as Type z which has 'Ray Hardy'.

Publisher: Argentine.

Lettering: Heavy, black, initial caps.

Reproduction: Lithograph.

BI-l-bi Cabeza de Ballena – Soud Georgia (LC), (Carcass of Whale – South Georgia).

Whale on flensing plan at the Cia. de Pesca land station, Grytviken, South Georgia.

Type bi

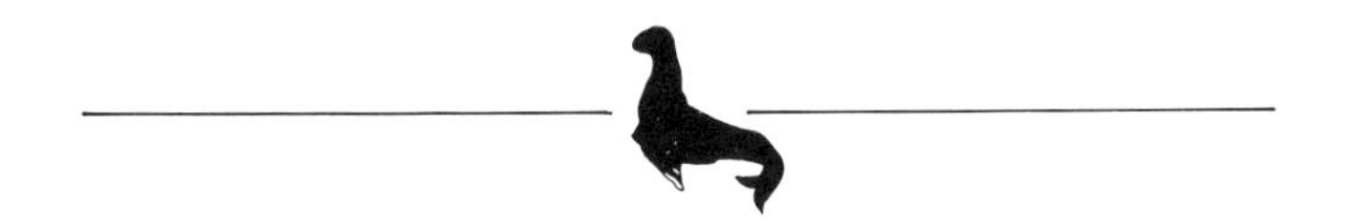

Series BJ	OVAL	1933

Publisher: In Great Britain.

Lettering: Very small Roman, initial caps, white.

Reproduction: Photograph.

BJ-l-bj Gentoo Penguins Nesting Falkland Islands (LC) Photo in oval.

BJ-l-bj

BJ

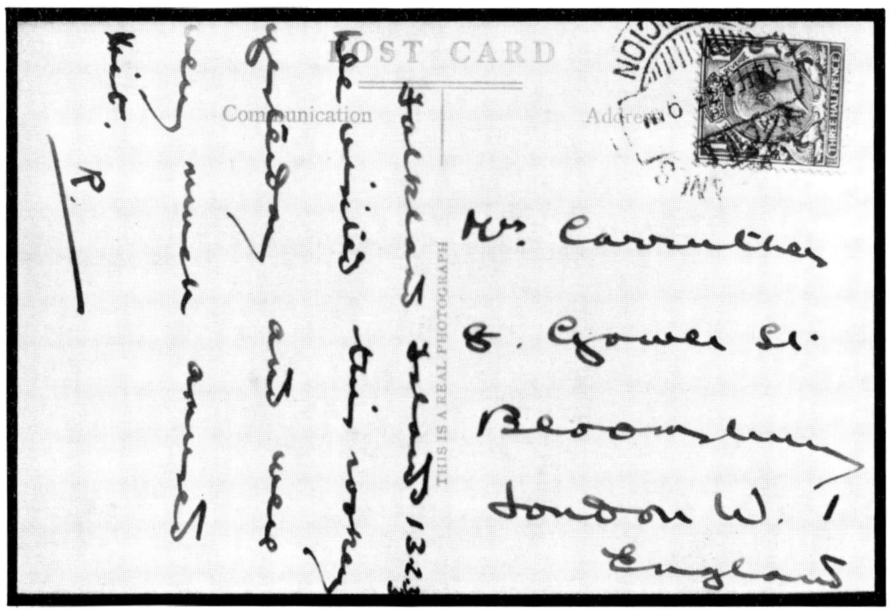
POST CARD
Communication
Address
THIS IS A REAL PHOTOGRAPH
Mrs. Carruthers
8. Gower St.
Bloomsbury
London W. 1
England

Type bj

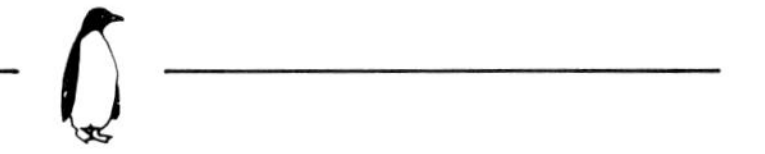

BK Series BK — WATTNE - LEITH HARBOUR — 1912

Publisher: Chr. Wattne, Norway (Also publisher of Series BE and BG).

Lettering: Very small, Roman, initial caps, white.

Reproduction: Unknown.

Comment: All of the postcards in this Series have the small title, 'Fra Leith Harbour, South Georgia'. Leith Harbour was owned and operated by the South Georgia Co., a subsidiary of Ch. Salvesen, Leith, Scotland. Salvesen's first whaling operation was at New Island in the Falklands but only lasted from 1908 to 1916. In 1916 the machinery was moved to Leith Harbour which Salvesen had operated since 1912 as a base for its factory ship 'Horatio'. However, in 1916 'Horatio' was destroyed by fire. Until 1966, Leith served both as a shore station and a base for floating factories. As at all stations a repair and maintenance crew overwintered there. Leith Harbour was the most northerly of three shore stations that opened onto Stromness Bay, the other two being Stromness Harbour, in the centre, operated by Sandefjord Whaling, Co., and Husvik Harbour, the most southerly, operated by Thonsbergs Hvafangeri. See AH-4-aqt for picture of New Island whaling station and Series AL for Husvik Harbour and Series BE, BF and BG for other postcards of Leith Harbour.

BK-1-bk

BK-1-bk Fra Leith Harbour, South Georgia (LL), Eneret Chr. Wattne (LR).
Catcher at left foreground.

BK-2-bk Fra Leith Harbour, South Georgia (LL), Eneret Chr. Wattne (LR).
Land station about 1910. Shows original factory which in 1911 was struck by an avalanche killing three workers. Because of the steep mountains that surrounded it Leith Harbour was avalanche prone. In addition to 1911 it was struck by an avalanche in 1929.

BK-3-bk Fra Leith Harbour, South Georgia (LL), Eneret Chr. Wattne (LR).
Oil storage tanks in center foreground. Barrels used to ship whale oil are stacked near center. Factory buildings at left centre.

BK-4-bk Fra Leith Harbour, South Georgia (LL), Eneret Chr. Wattne (LR).
View from land station at Leith Harbour looking east to Stromness Bay.

BK-5-bk Fra Leith Harbour, South Georgia (LL), Eneret Chr. Wattne (LR).
View looking south to Leith Harbour, in immediate foreground, then Stromness Harbour and finally Husvik Harbour beyond long point of land. It was the whaling station at Stromness, owned by Sandefjord Whaling Co., that Shackleton reached after his epic crossing of South Georgia, May 19–20, 1916.

BK-2-bk

BK

BK-3-bk

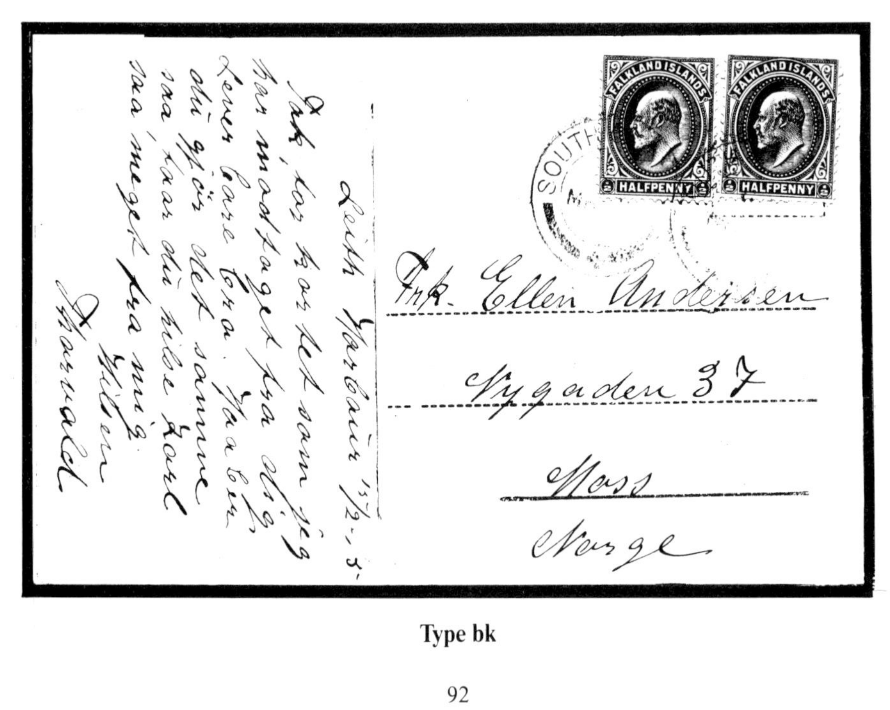

Type bk

BK

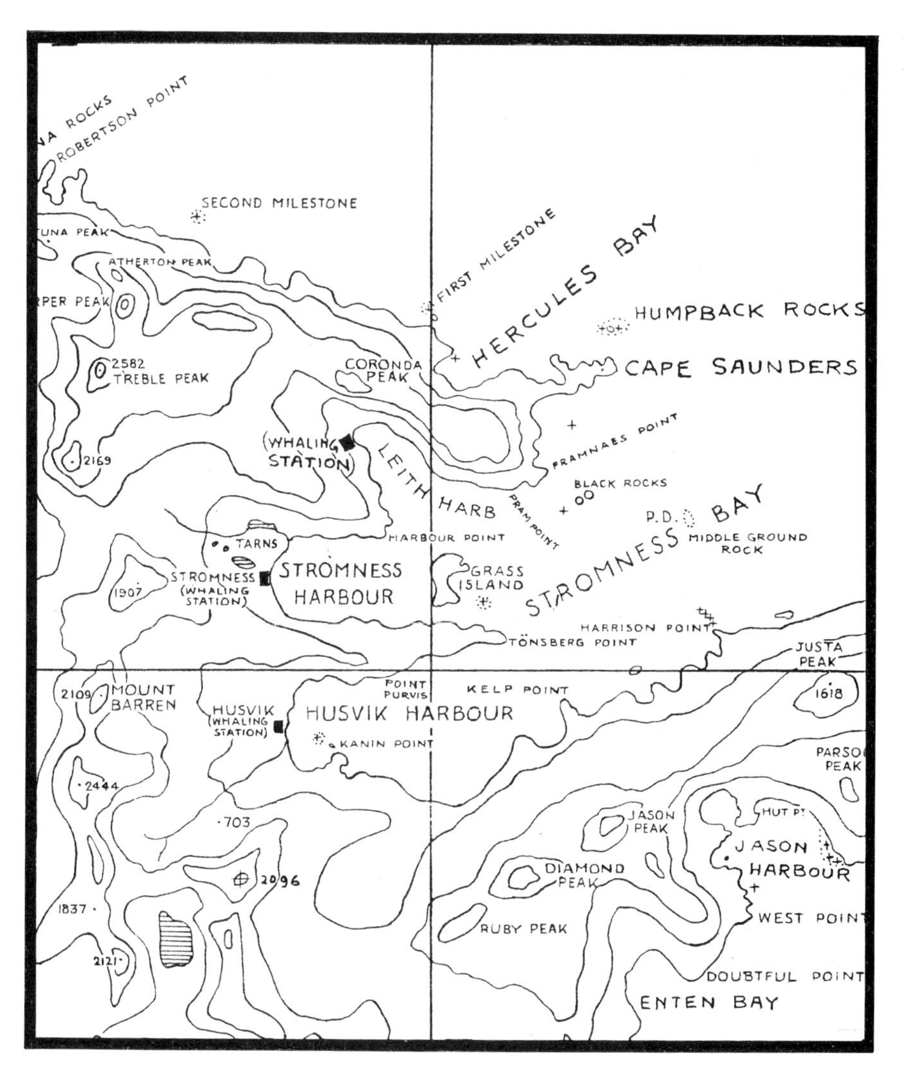

Stromness Bay, South Georgia
Whaling stations at Leith, Stromness and Husvik Harbours.

Publisher: S. M. Pettersen, Norway (Also publisher of Series Q).

Lettering: Roman, initial caps, black ink.

BL-l-bl Flensing of Hval (Flensing Whale) (LL).

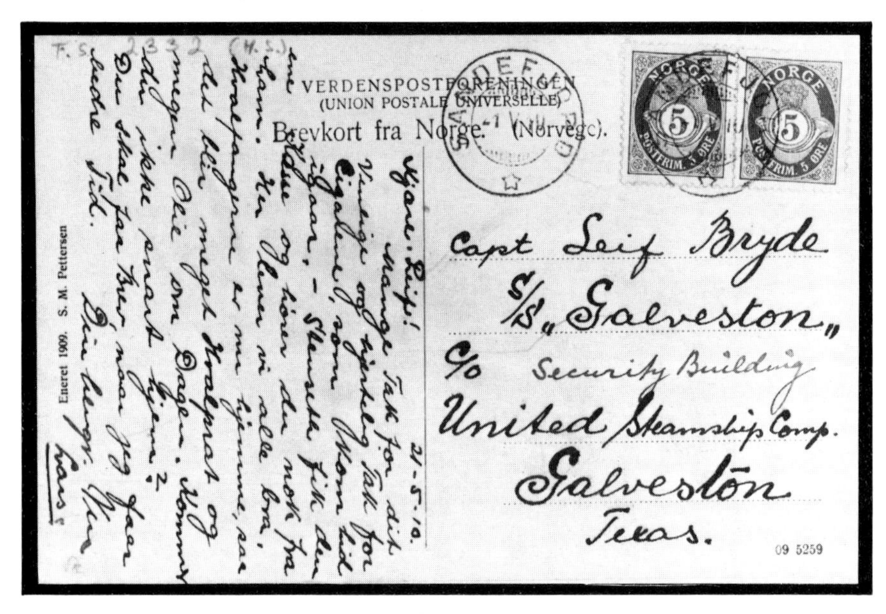

Type bl

Note: Six digit serial number at LR with space between first two and last four digits. Heading at UC reads: *VERDENSPOSTFORENINGEN (Union Postal Universelle) Brevkort fra Norge. (Norvege).*

Publisher: Argentine

Lettering: Black, initial caps.

BM-1-bm Recuerdo del Combate de 'Punta del Este' December 13, 1939 (R.O. del Uruguay), (Souvenir of the Battle of 'Punta del Este' December 13, 1939 (Oriental Republic of Uruguay).

Photo is identical to AQ-18-aqu *and* AQ-18-aqt *but with added title at LC in Spanish. Type is entirely different.*

Type bm

Publisher:	Foto Magn. Himberg, 'Southern Studio' Prince Olav Harbour, South Georgia. (Also published Series AF). *This postcard and Series AF were actually printed in South Georgia at the Southern Whaling and Sealing Co. land station, Prince Olav Harbour.*
Lettering	Modern, slanting to right, first letter caps.
Reproduction:	Photographic reproduction of black and white ink drawing.

BN-1-bn Foto. Himbergs Prospekt-kart over de Sydlige Hvalfangstfelter (Himberg Studio's Map of the S:outhern Whaling Grounds).

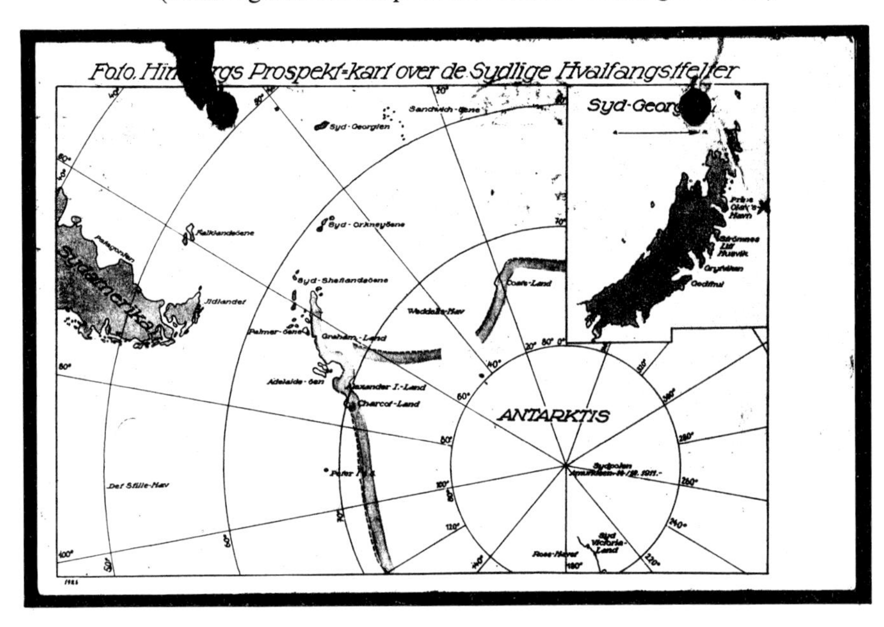

BN-1-bn

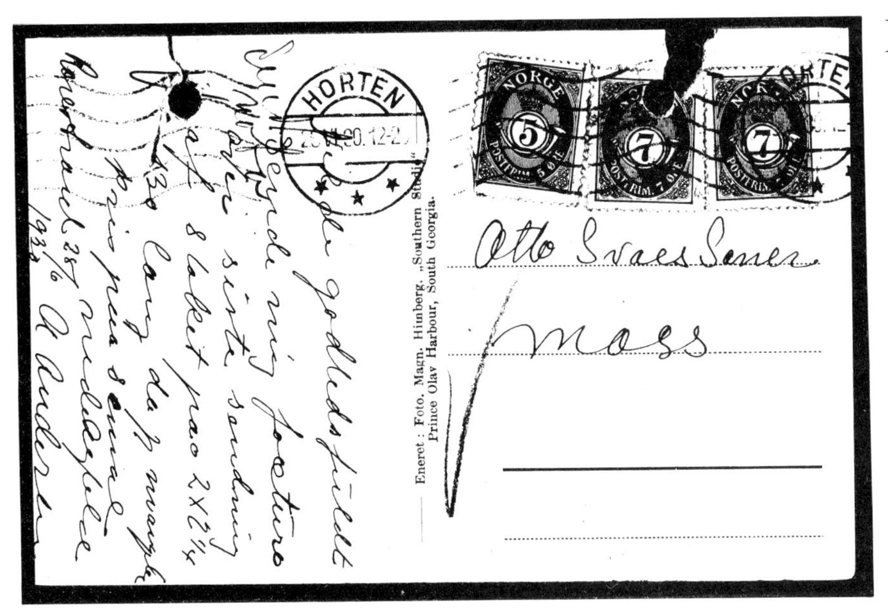
HORTEN
NORGE
Eneret: Foto. Magn. Himberg. „Southern Studio"
Prince Olav Harbour, South Georgia.

Type bn

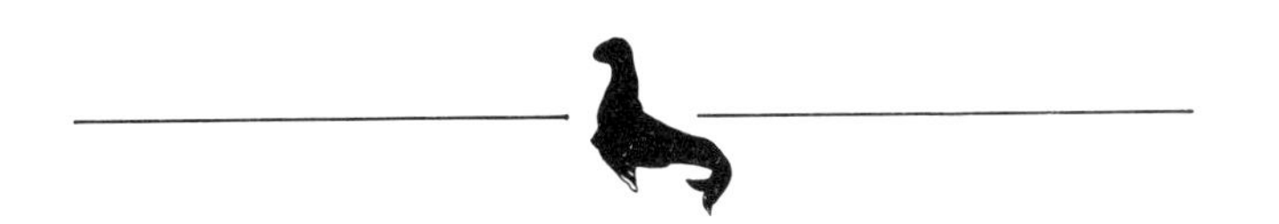

BO SERIES BO OPHELM 1915

Publisher: O. H. Ophelm, Norway.

Lettering: White, initial caps.

Reproduction: Photographic.

BO-1-bo Rensdyr. Syd Georgia (LL) (Reindeer, South Georgia), Eneret, O. H. Ophelm (LR).

Reindeer were introduced into South Georgia by Norwegians in 1911 when three bucks and seven does were liberated on the eastern shore of Cumberland Bay. A second herd was started in 1912 near Stromness Bay by the release of two bucks and five does, but their decendents were all killed by an avalanche in 1918. A third herd was started near Husvik Harbour in 1925. The two surviving herds have increased in size until they now total approximately 2,000. However they are prevented by intervening glaciers from merging. The reindeer provided both sport hunting and meat for the whalemen.

BO-2-bo Sjoelefanter i kamp (LL) (Elephant seals fighting). Eneret O.H. Ophelm (LR). Note: This is identical to LR title on BO-1-bo.

BO-1-bo

Type bo

Title Index

B

C

F

G

H

I

J

L

M

O

P

R

S

T

U

V

W

Subject Index

T

W

Y

Index of Publishers

Foto. Magn. Himberg, 'Southern Studio'.

Was owned and operated by Magnus Himberg (1880–c.1955), Himberg, Norway, probably during the whaling seasons 1921/1922 through 1930/1931. At Prince Olav Harbour he was a foreman for miscellaneous personnel. The photographs on the 'Southern Studio' postcards were taken and developed in South Georgia but the actual printing was probably done in Norway. He operated photo shops at a number of places in Norway beginning in Sandefjord in 1900 and continuing until his death at Lillesand.

,Southern Studio'
- Foto. Magn. Himberg -
Prince Olav Harbour, South Georgia

K.V. Lellman, Stanley. (Additional comment)

Some of K.V. Lellman's pen and ink postcards present a problem. The question is, how many cards of a particular design must have been reproduced and distributed in order to qualify as "published". Mr. Lellman reports that he did dozens of pen and ink sketches, some of which he "published" in quantity (in excess of 50), whereas others were issued singly or to a small circle of friends. Many of these Lellman works of art have been received by the authors since publication of the original Catalogue and a judgment has been made as to whether these "new" cards constitute published items. It was determined that none did although the authors believe that those shown in the original Catalogue (Series AX and BA) qualify as "published" items. A few examples of these Lellman non-published postcards are shown at right.

Chr. Wattne, probably of Sandefjord, Norway.

Published postcards of Leith Harbour, South Georgia for sale to whalers. See Series BE, BG and BK

O.H. Ophelm, Norway.

Known to have published postcards of South Georgia. See Series BO.

FALKLAND ISLANDS DEPENDENCIES
POSTAGE & REVENUE
Graham Land
10 FEB 1947
17 JAN 1946
24 FEB 1947
22 MAR 1949

Postcards of the Falkland Islands, A Catalogue: 1900–1950

by Henry and Frances Heyburn

Reviews and Comments

As a thorough piece of research into a specific area covered by picture postcards, it is difficult to imagine this book being bettered, and it's worth buying, both for its intrinsic interest and for its style of presentation.
Picture Postcard Monthly

Great news for Falkland Islands enthusiasts, and this includes those who also collect Antarctic areas. A much needed and very well done book ... Illustrations are sharp and the quality of the book itself is excellent.
Canadian Stamp News

This is a truly remarkable work. Breaking new ground, Henry and Frances Heyburn are to be congratulated on having identified and described in detail over 340 postcards of the Falkland Islands and South Georgia up to 1950.
R. N. Spafford, Falkland Islands Newsletter

To describe this book as a 'catalogue' is a misnomer as it is as much a social history of the Islands and Dependencies, as a listing of cards ... A most beautifully produced volume of 255 pages, profusely illustrated and containing very detailed notes on the people, places and history of the Falklands.
Upland Goose (Falkland Islands Philatelic Study Group)

They are to be commended for their relentless search for these bits of polar postal history, and for their self-discipline in not rushing into print, thus giving us what this reviewer regards as a comprehensive delineation of these fascinating collectors' items.
Bernard V. Coyne in 'Ice Cap News'

It is obvious that it is going to be a standard work of reference on Falkland Island matters ... You have now established a very unique part of our heritage which will hopefully inspire others to continue in other fields.
John Smith, Stanley, Falkland Islands

You have truly created knowledge where none existed before.

Your book was a pure delight. What more can I say than well done.

A surge of philatelic interest followed in the wake of the conflict in the South Atlantic, and by now those newcomers to the field may be getting restless for a new tack to take in their postal history collections. This volume is highly recommended and is certainly a must have for perennial Falklands fans. Unlike many philatelic tomes, this one could also find a comfortable fit in the family bookcase, able to provoke the interest and imaginations of younger members of the family in search of school-project ideas or some (heaven forbid!) 'worthwhile' leisure reading. An efficient cataloguing system devised by the authors regiments the book which is laid out for very easy reference. Any number of stamp specialty catalogues could take a good lesson from the layout, as well as from the intelligent organization of the numbering system.

'The American Philatelist'

This is a remarkable compilation which treats what might be considered a very narrow theme very broadly. Thus, through investigation and discussion of postcards with their messages and details of postal transmission, a fascinating amount of the history, social matters, and other aspects of the Falkland Islands and Dependencies is revealed. The catalogue is ... very comprehensive. I found it fascinating. I would give the book a particularly strong recommendation to visitors to the region.

R. W. Headland of Scott Polar Research Institute in 'Polar Record'

Publisher; and Distributors in Great Britain and U.S.A.:

PICTON PUBLISHING
Queensbridge Cottages, Patterdown
Chippenham, Wilts SN15 2NS
Telephone: (0249) 443430

Price £14.95
U.K. postage and packing £1
Wholesale prices on application

HAWLEY-COOKE BOOKSELLERS
27 Shelbyville Road Plaza
Louisville, Ky 40207

HENRY HEYBURN, a life long Kentuckian, says: 'I've been in love with the Falklands since I was twelve years old and have collected, read, corresponded and travelled in their orbit ever since'. During the Argentine Occupation he and his wife, Frances, formed the Kentucky Committee for the Falkland Islands which raised and distributed over $4,500 to various Falkland related organisations. A graduate of Harvard College and Harvard Law School, he is a Senior Partner in one of Kentucky's largest law firms; a former member of the Kentucky General Assembly, Chancellor of the Episcopal Diocese of Kentucky and Regent of Kentucky State University. His collecting interests centre on the Falklands, but also include St. Helena, Ascension and Guam. He is a member of the Falkland Island Philatelic Study Group, Polar Postal History Society of Great Britain, American Society of Polar Philatelists and the Antarctican Society.

FRANCES HEYBURN, is also a native Kentuckian and a member of the Class of 1947 at Smith College. She is an ardent and locally ranked tennis player, organic gardener, geneologist, and traveller. She and her husband share a love of islands. In addition to the Falklands, South Georgia and the South Shetlands, they have visited St. Helena, the Galapagos, Lundy, Tristan de Cunha and many others. The Heyburns have four grown children and three grandchildren.

They have collaborated to produce what they see as much more than just a catalogue of Falkland postcards – with all that word connotates in attention to detail – but also a living, breathing social history of the people, places and wildlife of those far-away islands.

Additional Bibliography

Specialized Stamp Catalogue of the Falkland Islands and Dependencies Including Postal History and Cancellations 1800-1987 — Stefan Heijtz, Box 26048, S-10041 Stockholm, Sweden

Postcards of the Falkland Islands, A Catalogue: 1900–1950 — Henry and Frances Heyburn, Picton Publishing, Bath Road, Chippenham, Wilts. SN15 2AB

Your Turn!

We will be most grateful to any of our readers for ...

⋆ Additional Cards
(Please send xerox copy of front and back)

⋆ Corrections ⋆ Suggestions

⋆ Additional information ⋆ Questions???

We look forward to hearing from you.

Just write your information and mail to:

Henry and Frances Heyburn
3918 Leland Road
Louisville, Kentucky 40207 U.S.A.